Todah, Teacher!

A Fill-in-the-Blanks Book of Thanks

By _____
and Sari Kopitnikoff

Ideastrator
Press

Todah, Teacher!
A Fill-in-the-Blanks Book of Thanks

Copyright ©2023 by Sari Kopitnikoff

ISBN 979-8-9851605-4-3, paperback

Published by Ideastrator Press, New Jersey

The author welcomes feedback at sari@thatjewishmoment.com.

How to Use This Book

If you're the teacher, skip this page, and go ahead and read what's inside! You do sacred work, and this is one small way to thank you for the hours and the heart you put into your teaching.

If you're the student, get ready to thank your teacher in a fun and meaningful way. All you have to do is get some coloring utensils and think back on your year — and you're ready to bring this book to life. You can choose to write your answers, draw them, or do a combination of the two. Feel free to change any of the prompts to better fit your needs. Have fun with it! And realize that you're doing the beautiful *mitzvah* of *hakarat hatov*, showing appreciation. Your small token of thanks will go a long way in letting your teacher know how much they mean to you.

Finally, thank you so much to the following educators and editors who helped make this book a reality: Lisa Bernstein, Fran Besalel, Shirley Cohen, Stacey Gay, Gail Greenberg, Shana Lee, Aaron Levitt, Sarah Levy, Rachel Mussaf, Shelly Rauchwerger, and Sue Rosman.

Dear _____,

This book is for you, my teacher.

You have given me knowledge, you have given me skills, and you have helped me nurture my *middot*/character traits. And those are some of the greatest gifts possible — because I can carry them with me throughout life.

Thank you for everything you have done this year to help me learn.

I hope you appreciate this small expression of my gratitude.

Sincerely,

_____

Many Thanks!

I decorated these phrases for you...

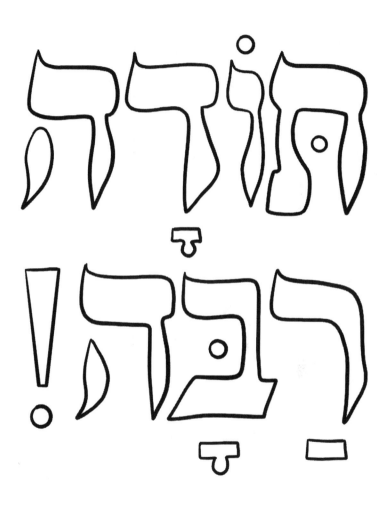

to thank you for all that you've done.

Torah Teacher Texts

חֲנֹךְ לַנַּעַר, עַל-פִּי דַרְכּוֹ...

Train a child, according to the path they should go...

-Proverbs: 22:6

Thank you for encouraging me to take the right path for *me*.

I have so many things I want to thank you for. Here are just a few:

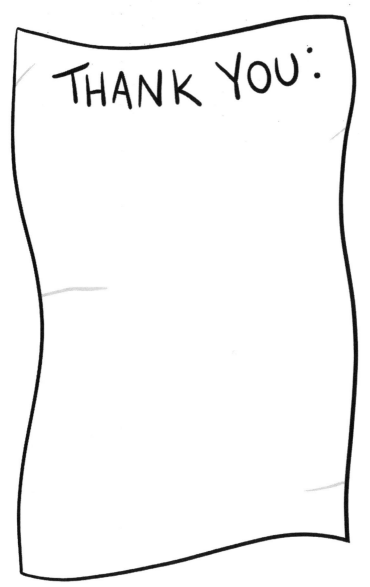

BEFORE...

This is what I was like at the
beginning of the school year...

AFTER!

And this is what I'm like now,
after learning so much from you!

If people would ask me to describe
you in three words, I'd say:

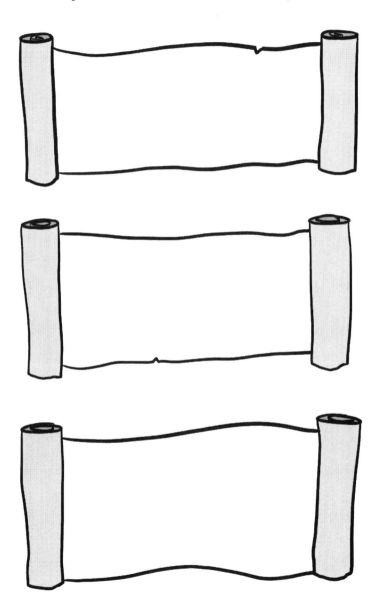

And if they begggged me for a fourth word, I'd add:

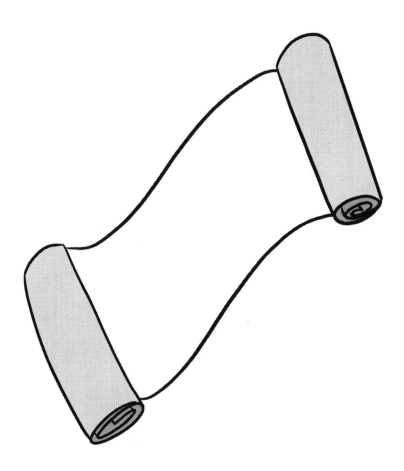

Torah Teacher Texts

רַבִּי אֶלְעָזָר בֶּן שַׁמּוּעַ אוֹמֵר, יְהִי כְּבוֹד תַּלְמִידְךָ חָבִיב עָלֶיךָ כְּשֶׁלְּךָ ...

Rabbi Elazar ben Shammua says, "Let the honor of your student be as dear to you as your own..."

-Pirkei Avot: 4:12

Thank you for honoring me as a student!

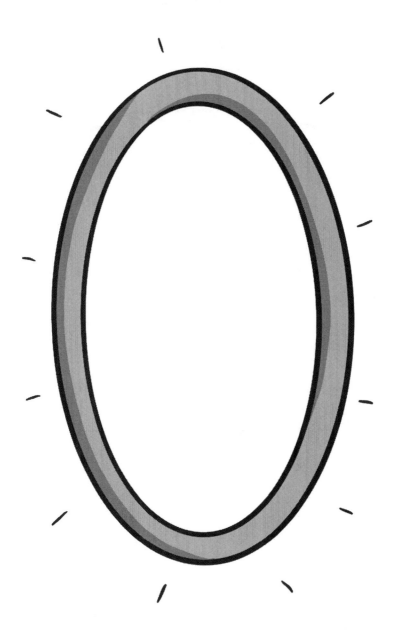

Here's my portrait of you!

Something I learned from you that I
will always remember:

Something you said that
really stuck with me:

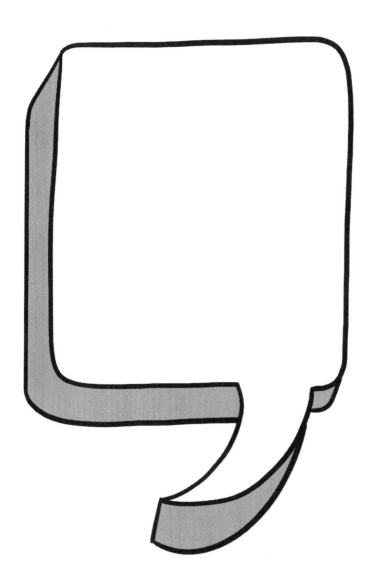

It made me feel really special
when you...

Torah Teacher Texts

בֶּן זוֹמָא אוֹמֵר, אֵיזֶהוּ חָכָם הַלּוֹמֵד מִכָּל אָדָם.

Ben Zoma says, "Who is wise? The one who learns from every person."

-Pirkei Avot: 4:1

I learned a lot from you, and I thank you for learning from me.

This is something I enjoyed
doing with you this year.

Here's something I will really miss about being in your class.

What I would tell your future students about having you as a teacher:

But if you ever want to take a break from teaching, you'd make a great...

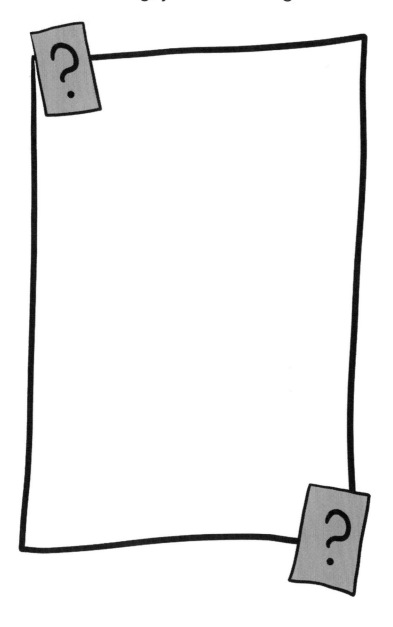

ᴛᴏʀᴀʜ ᴛᴇᴀᴄʜᴇʀ ᴛᴇxᴛs

רַבִּי עֲקִיבָא אוֹמֵר: מִנַּיִן שֶׁחַיָּיב אָדָם לִשְׁנוֹת לְתַלְמִידוֹ עַד שֶׁיִּלְמָדֶנּוּ — שֶׁנֶּאֱמַר: "וְלַמְּדָהּ אֶת בְּנֵי יִשְׂרָאֵל."

Rabbi Akiva says, "How do we know that a person is required to teach their student until they learn and understand the material?" As it says, "And teach it to the children of Israel."

-Eruvin 54B: 14

Thank you for your patience with me this year.

Though it's the end of the book, my appreciation doesn't end. Thank you so much for teaching me and for the lasting impacts you've made on my life.

With much gratitude,

_____

About the Author/Artist

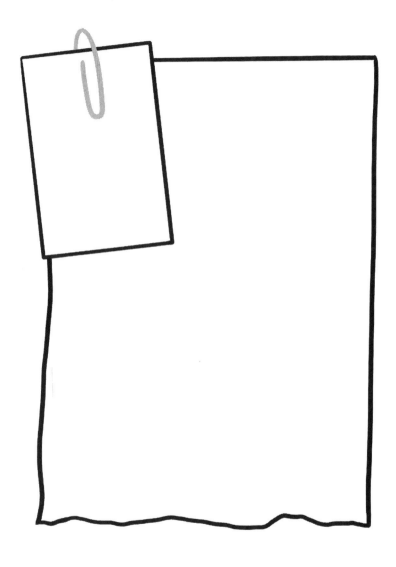

About the Other Author

As a student, Sari loved spending time making special thank you cards for her teachers. Then, when she became an educator, she realized how much those probably meant to her teachers.

Sari is an experiential educator, digital artist, educational performer, and content creator. She is passionate about creating books, games, activities, shows, virtual challenges, and interactive workshops that bring Judaism to life.

You can follow Sari's work on Instagram, Facebook, and TikTok @ThatJewishMoment, and you can find lots of free Jewish educational materials at ThatJewishMoment.com. There, you can book Sari for a live or virtual workshop, sign up for her newsletter, or just say hi.

Other books by Sari:

That Jewish Moment
My Davening Diary
Jewmagine That!
My Escape from Egypt
Only Kidding!
Counting Up

Made in the USA
Middletown, DE
07 January 2024

47366289R00015